Cardinals Care was established to give fans a way of teaming up with Cardinals players and the organization to help children in our community – both on and off the baseball field. Since it was established in 1997, Cardinals Care has distributed nearly $21 million to support St. Louis area non-profit youth organizations and built 21 youth ball fields in local under-resourced neighborhoods. 2015 marks the 12th year of Cardinals Care's innovative Redbird Rookies program, a free baseball league for kids who otherwise might not have the opportunity to play. In addition to providing all the uniforms, gloves, bats, balls and other equipment needed for each team, Redbird Rookies also provides extensive off-field support in the areas of health, education, mentoring and the cultural arts for each of the nearly 4,500 kids who participate in the program each year. To learn more about all of Cardinals Care's programs visit cardinals.com/community.

A PORTION FROM THE SALE OF EACH BOOK IS DONATED
TO CARDINALS CARE

"This book is dedicated
to my parents."

-Fredbird

How FREDBIRD Became a REDBIRD

Based on the book
THE LEGEND OF FREDBIRD
by Steven Kveton

Illustrated by Gabhor Utomo
Book design by Josh Taggert

Fredbird was a Redbird rooter
from the day he was born.

His mom and pop were great Cardinal fans. Soon baby Fredbird was chirping for the Cards at the ballpark.

Like all little birds, Fredbird dreamed of playing for the St. Louis Cardinals...

and winning the World Series!

Under his father's wing, Fredbird...

learned the finer points of the game

Fredbird's mom taught him
that baseball was fun...

even though it hurt sometimes.

After playing lots of catch, Fredbird was called up as the Cards' rookie right fielder.

The friendly Fredbird quickly became the fans' favorite Redbird.

But the pitcher didn't throw like Mom or Pop. Fredbird struck out every time.

And pop flies kept bouncing off his beak.

Then in the eighth inning he
tripped over the foul line.

Things looked bleak for the Birds in
the ninth. Fredbird was up and the
Cards were down.

VISITORS   2
CARDINALS   0

One...two...three pitches and he was out. The fans sighed with every swing.

"If the crowd can't cheer for me," Fredbird thought, "maybe they'll cheer with me."

Perched on the dugout roof,
Fredbird led the fans in a big
Cardinal YA-HOO. The crowd
roared and the team scored.

The Redbirds flocked around Fredbird
and carried him off the field.
Fredbird helped win the game.

Since that day, Fredbird has been the Cardinals MVB (Most Valuable Bird).

St. Louis Cardinals N.L. Pennants

Year	Record	Manager
1926	89-65	Rogers Hornsby
1928	95-59	Bill McKechnie
1930	92-62	Gabby Street
1931	101-53	Gabby Street
1934	95-58	Frankie Frisch
1942	106-48	Billy Southworth
1943	105-49	Billy Southworth
1944	105-49	Billy Southworth
1946	98-58	Eddie Dyer
1964	93-69	Johnny Keane
1967	101-60	Red Schoendienst
1968	97-65	Red Schoendienst
1982	92-79	Whitey Herzog
1985	101-61	Whitey Herzog
1987	95-67	Whitey Herzog
2004	105-57	Tony La Russa
2006	83-78	Tony La Russa
2011	90-72	Tony La Russa
2013	97-65	Mike Matheny

St. Louis Cardinals World Championships

Year	Opponent	Manager
1926	New York	Rogers Hornsby
1931	Philadelphia	Gabby Street
1934	Detroit	Frankie Frisch
1942	New York	Billy Southworth
1944	St. Louis	Billy Southworth
1946	Boston	Eddie Dyer
1964	New York	Johnny Keane
1967	Boston	Red Schoendienst
1982	Milwaukee	Whitey Herzog
2006	Detroit	Tony La Russa
2011	Texas	Tony La Russa

 Washington

Montana

North Dakota

Oregon

Idaho

South Dakota

Wyoming

 Nebraska

Nevada

Utah

Colorado

Kansas

California

Arizona

New Mexico

Okl

Texas

GO CARDS!

Major League
Baseball

Maine

Minnesota

Wisconsin

Michig

New York

Vt.

N.H.

Mass

Iowa

Illinois

Indiana

Ohio

Pennsylvania

Missouri

Kentucky

West
Virginia

Virginia

North Carolina

Arkansas

Tennessee

South Carolina

Mississippi

Georgia

Alabama

Louisiana

Florida

AMERICAN LEAGUE

AL EAST

 Baltimore Orioles

 Boston Red Sox

 New York Yankees

 Tampa Bay Rays

 Toronto Blue Jays

AL Central

- Chicago White Sox
- Cleveland Indians
- Detroit Tigers
- Kansas City Royals
- Minnesota Twins

AL West

- Los Angeles Angels
- Oakland Athletics
- Houston Astros
- Seattle Mariners
- Texas Rangers

NL East

 Atlanta Braves

 Miami Marlins

 New York Mets

 Philadelphia Phillies

 Washington Nationals

NL Central

Chicago Cubs

Cincinnati Reds

Milwaukee Brewers

Pittsburgh Pirates

St. Louis Cardinals

NL West

Arizona Diamondbacks

Colorado Rockies

Los Angeles Dodgers

San Diego Padres

San Francisco Giants

Marty Hendin

March 16, 1948 – January 12, 2008

Like the character of Fredbird he helped to bring to life, Marty Hendin loved the Cardinals as much in adulthood as he did as a child. As Community Relations Director, Marty was the boy who got his dream job. He worked tirelessly to make each game a memorable experience from pre-game ceremonies to promotions and fireworks. He connected players and fans at the Winter Warm-Up, the Cardinal Caravan, and on Cardinal Cruises. He was also instrumental in developing outreach programs like Cardinals Care and involving players in numerous charities. In 1983, Marty hired me as the team announcer at the ballpark. It was an absolute pleasure to work with him. He was enthusiastic about the Cardinals every day and had a lovable persona about him that made it impossible for anyone to say no to him. Sadly, Marty left us too soon but he will always be remembered with a smile. This book is a tribute to my friend and a true Cardinal Classic: Marty Hendin.

-John Ulett

Autographs